DEVELOPING COMPREHENSION

Orange Book

Alan Lynskey

Margaret Stillie

STANLEY THORNES

Contents

	page
Introduction	4
Ninety-nine dragons	
Ninety-nine Dragons Barbara Sleigh	6
Brothers	
All About the Bullerby Children	
Astrid Lindgren	8
Children	
Looking at History R. J. Unstead	10
Cat in school	
The Worst Kids in the World	
B. Robinson	12
Chocolate raisin clusters	
Sequencing	14
Bubble and Squeak	
The Battle of Bubble and Squeak	
Philippa Pearce	16
Handsome Hare	
Sequencing from	
How the Whale Became and other stories	
Ted Hughes	18
Mrs Smith's cupboard	
Picture comprehension	19
Spider and the pot	
More Adventures of Spider	
Joyce C. Arkhurst	20
Eruptions	
Volcanoes William Hirst	22

Paddington hits out
Paddington Goes to Town   Michael Bond   24

Your first dog
Cloze text from *Your First Dog*
Paul Collan and Steffi Fields   26

Helen Keller
Cloze text from *Helen Keller*
Margaret Davidson   27

The chocolate factory
Charley and the Chocolate Factory
Roald Dahl   28

Indian war bonnets   30

The magic sweets
Grasshopper and the Unwise Owl
Jim Slater   32

Woodland creatures
Chart   34

The poor man and the doctor
The Secret Shoemakers   J. Reeves   36

The magic finger
The Magic Finger   Roald Dahl   38

Persephone
Freda Saxey   40

Grooming
Sequencing   42

Detective Lucy
Lucy   Catherine Storr   44

The witch who lived on the motorway
The Magician Who Kept a Pub
Dorothy Edwards   46

Introduction

Developing Comprehension is an attempt to clarify and to develop the many skills involved in the real comprehension of language.

The Barrett taxonomy, on which the series is based, presents five main categories of comprehension.

1 Literal comprehension: answering questions by direct reference to the text. These answers are usually explicitly stated in the passage.

2 Reorganisational comprehension: classifying, collecting and organising information explicitly stated in the passage. The information may be collected from more than one source.

3 Inferential comprehension: detecting information implied in a passage. This demands thinking and deduction beyond what appears in the passage.

4 Evaluative comprehension: interpreting and evaluating the writer's assumptions or intentions, often by comparison with the reader's own experiences or opinions.

5 Appreciative comprehension: responding to a passage with enjoyment, and with an awareness of its language usage and emotion.

Obviously these skills are not clear cut and separate. There is a considerable overlap between categories. Certainly the higher-level skills — the ability to appreciate and evaluate written material — require the child to exercise literal and re-organisational skills in order to reach decisions.

Techniques

Developing Comprehension uses a variety of techniques to develop reading skills:

Prediction

Predictions are vital to the reader's active involvement in what he or she is reading. In the exercises we ask "What do you think happens next?" In the classroom children should be asked to discuss their predictions and the evidence which supports them. Teachers can give more practice in prediction by breaking a passage into sections and asking "Where do you think this is happening?" "What will so-and-so do next?" "What will happen then?". When the next section is read, the children can evaluate and revise their predictions in the light of what they have learnt.

Cloze texts

These are passages with words omitted, which children are asked to supply. Often there is no right or wrong answer. The child is asked to supply the best word he or she can think of which contributes to the meaning and the feeling of the passage. If the chosen word can be justified, then it can be judged as right. Sometimes the missing word will be determined by the structure of the sentence, and there will be little argument. But in every case, discussion of alternatives and reasons for choices is vital to the learning process.

Sequencing and ordering

The child is asked to place events in order or sequence. Technically, he or she will need to be able to pick up indicator clues (next, but, etc.) which relate one paragraph to another, and then comprehend the underlying pattern of a passage — to understand across whole paragraphs the development of events. These passages are especially valuable when used in small group discussion. Some whole-class oral work will complete the lesson.

Evaluation

The teacher needs to have clear purposes of evaluation. *Developing Comprehension* is designed to evaluate and improve children's ability to read and fully comprehend. Answers, therefore, should be evaluated initially by the way they display the child's understanding and appreciation of what he or she has read. Class room discussions should begin with meaning, before looking at how to record that meaning in written English.

The work produced, written or oral, indicates to the teacher the strengths and weaknesses of each child. Programmes of work can be developed to cater for the weaknesses of individuals or groups of children.

The evaluation of responses to cloze texts and prediction and sequencing exercises will be oral as comparisons are made and reasons put forward as to why one choice is better or worse than another. Discussion sessions are crucial in helping children to see what they have missed in their reading, and they encourage purposeful re-reading, which is a vital higher-level skill.

Marking and assessment

The responses or answers a child makes are a starting point for teaching, not a final assessment. Even a totally inappropriate answer will provide a basis on which to work.

The level of difficulty of a passage in relation to a child's reading level must be taken into account in any assessment. No child can be expected to make an evaluation or appreciation of a passage he or she can read only with difficulty. But teacher expectation is a significant factor in pupils' attainment and should not be pitched too low.

We have chosen passages of high literary merit, including the best writers of contemporary children's fiction. We hope that children will be encouraged to read more of the work of the writers they have enjoyed.

ALAN LYNSKEY
MARGARET STILLIE

Ninety-nine dragons

Two children cannot get to sleep. Their daddy tells them to try counting sheep jumping over a gate. Ben thinks sheep are soppy. He counts dragons.

"Eighty-eight, eighty-nine," counted Ben, sleepily.

Now when he reached dragon ninety-eight he was almost asleep, and dragon ninety-nine was very small indeed; not much bigger than a kitten. But it clapped its
5 flippers together bravely, as the others had done, blew a couple of sparks and a tiny thread of smoke through its nostrils, and jumped with a "Whoops!" which was little more than a squeak. But instead of sailing over the gate as its companions had done, it stumbled against the great
10 high gate, and fell back, plop! right on to the middle of Ben's bed, with a sad little "Wheee!" and a slight smell of singeing.

Ben shot up in bed, very wide awake all at once. He stared at the little dragon over the hump of his knees, and
15 the little dragon stared back, and I don't know which of them was the more surprised.

There was a long pause, and then Ben said:

"Hadn't you better go after the others?"

"How can I?" said Dragon Ninety-nine. "That great
20 iron gate is too high for me to jump over. They've all gone without me. Whatever shall I do?"

To Ben's horror two tears welled up from its slanting golden eyes, and trickled down its long green nose, to dry with a sizzle when they reached its smoking nostrils.
25 "Even if I could get over the gate I should never catch

up with the others, not with my short legs. They're all bigger than me," it went on unhappily.

Ninety-nine Dragons
Barbara Sleigh

1 Where did the dragon land?
2 What colour and shape were the dragon's eyes?
3 What was the gate made of?
4 How did the little dragon get ready to jump over the gate?
5 What happens to the dragon's tears?
6 Write down everything you can find which tells what the dragon looks like.
·7 Why couldn't the little dragon get over the gate?
8 Why is there a smell of singeing when the dragon lands on the bed?
9 How does Ben feel when the dragon starts to cry?
10 How would you feel if a young dragon landed on your bed?
11 What do you do when you can't get to sleep? What would you count to send you to sleep?
12 Find these words in the passage. What do they mean?

· couple(line 6)   companions(line 9)
  hump(line14)   slanting(line 22)
  singeing(line12)

Brothers

Sometimes when I get tired of Lars and Pip I think that it would be better not to have any brothers at all. They tease me when I play with my dolls; they're always hitting me; and they always say that it's my turn to dry the

5 dishes. Lars once told Mother that he couldn't understand why anyone should have wanted to have a girl. It would have been much better to have had nine more boys, so they could have enough for a soccer team.

10 But Mother said, "I am so happy to have my little girl. I don't know what I'd do without her. But nine more boys! It's quite enough with you two."

So Lars didn't get anywhere with his stupid suggestion.

But sometimes it's nice to have brothers — when we

15 have pillow fights at night, when they come into my room and tell ghost stories, and when it's Christmas and things like that. And once Pip stood up for me when a boy in school hit me because I pushed him by mistake. Pip hit him back and said, "Don't you ever do that again!"

20 "Well, she doesn't have to push me," said Ben. That was the other boy's name.

"That wasn't her fault. She didn't see you. She doesn't have eyes in the back of her head, stupid," said Pip.

My, how I liked Pip then! So it really isn't too bad to

25 have brothers, but, of course, it would be better to have sisters.

All About the Bullerby Children
Astrid Lindgren

1 What things does the writer say are nice about having brothers?
2 What things does she say are not so nice?
3 When does the writer think it would be better not to have brothers at all?
4 Why did the boy Ben hit the girl?
5 Why did mother say she didn't want nine more boys?
6 Why did Lars want nine more boys in the family?
7 Why do you think the girl said Lars's suggestion was "stupid"?
8 Why do you think Pip hit the boy back?
9 How did his sister feel about what Pip did?
10 Why do you think she still thinks at the end that it would be better to have sisters?
11 Sometimes the writer likes her brothers and sometimes she doesn't. Talk about things or people you like *sometimes*.
12 Do you think brothers and sisters should stand up for each other?

Children

Many years ago, at the time of King John and Richard the Lionheart, children were not treated as they are now. In those days parents were very strict with their children and beat them for any misbehaviour. Even when they
5 were quite grown up, they could not do as they wished, but had to obey their parents.

The sons of nobles were sent to another lord when they were seven years old. They lived in his manor or castle as pages, learning good manners and how to wait
10 at table. The girls learned how to manage a big house and how to make medicines from herbs, called simples.

They also did beautiful needlework and spinning, and in time the unmarried ones were called spinsters.

Parents arranged marriages without asking their
15 children. Girls were often married at fourteen or sixteen, and it was quite a disgrace to be unmarried at twenty.

There were a few schools (such as Eton and Winchester) but rich men's children were more often taught at home by a tutor, who was a monk or a family
20 priest. He took prayers at home and usually wrote all the letters.

Peasants' children did not go to school, but a few were sent to the monastery as novices, to be trained as monks.

Sometimes priests taught the children Bible stories in
25 the church porch.

By the time peasants' children were seven years old, most of them were minding the animals and helping their parents.

Looking at History
R. J. Unstead

1 What happened to children if they did not do as they were told?
2 Who were pages and what did they do?
3 What was a "simple"?
4 How did the daughters of nobles spend their time?
5 How were rich children educated?
6 How did poor children learn about God?
7 How old were poor children when they started work?
8 Compare how poor and rich children lived. Would you rather have been rich or poor? Why?
9 What was the only way a poor boy could learn to read and write?
10 Find these words in the passage. Look them up in your dictionary. Write the word and its meaning in the passage.

strict(line 3)   nobles(line 7)   manor(line 8)
page(line 9)   herbs(line 11)   tutor(line 19)
monk(line 23)   priest(line 20)   peasant(line 22)
porch(line 25)

Cat in school

This is part of an American story. "First grade" is what Americans call the first infant class at school. "Show-and-Tell" is a lesson where children take interesting things to school, show them to the rest of the class and talk about them. Claude didn't need to tell anything!

One day Claude Herdman emptied the whole first grade in three minutes flat when he took the cat to Show-and-Tell. He didn't feed it for two days so it was already mad, and then he carried it to school in a box, and when
5 he opened the box the cat shot right out — straight up in the air, people said.

It came down on the top blackboard ledge and clawed four big long scratches all the way down the blackboard. Then it just tore around all over the place, scratching little
10 kids and shedding fur and scattering books and papers everywhere.

The teacher, Miss Brandel, yelled for everybody to run out in the hall, and she pulled a coat over her head and grabbed a broom and tried to corner the cat. But of
15 course she couldn't see, with the coat over her head, so she just ran up and down the aisles, hollering "Here, kitty!" and smacking the broom down whenever the cat hissed back. She knocked over the Happy Family dollhouse and the globe of the world, and broke the
20 aquarium full of twenty gallons of water and about sixty-five goldfish.

All the time she kept yelling for Claude to come and catch his cat, but Claude had gone out in the hall with the rest of the class.

The Worst Kids in the World
B. Robinson

1 How did Claude get the cat to school?
2 Where did the cat land after it was released?
3 Who did the cat belong to?
4 Write down all the damage the *cat* did to the classroom.
5 Write down all the damage *Miss Brandel* did as she tried to catch the cat.
6 Why do you think Claude didn't feed the cat before he took it to school?
7 Why do you think Claude didn't try to catch his cat?
8 Why do you think Miss Brandel put a coat over her head?
9 Read the words in this list. Write down the ones which you think fit Claude.

   kind   helpful   mischievous
   amusing   well mannered   disobedient

10 Find one word in the passage which means

   (a) marks made by something sharp
   (b) a place for keeping fish
   (c) a sphere showing countries and oceans
   (d) shouting loudly
   (e) the space between rows of desks.

11 Think about how Miss Brandel, Claude and the class felt during the cat's mad escapade.
Write down four words for each which you think might describe these feelings. The first one is begun for you.

Miss Brandel	1. surprised	2.	3.	4.
Claude	1.	2.	3.	4.
The class	1.	2.	3.	4.

Chocolate raisin clusters

Here is a recipe for chocolate raisin clusters. It is not in the right order. Read it, and then decide which order the pictures and writing should be in.

Write out your order using the letters on the pictures. Talk with your friends about the order you have decided on.

A
Stand the basin over the saucepan, and make sure it is steady.

B
Turn off the heat, and lift the basin from the saucepan. *Use oven gloves.*

C
Choose a basin that fits over the saucepan and is big enough to mix everything together.

D
Heat the boiling ring or hotplate.

E
Break the chocolate into the basin.

F

Add more cornflakes, stir again. Continue like this until you have a nice chocolate-covered mixture. You may not need all the cornflakes.

G

Leave the clusters for an hour or until hard, then put on the serving plate.

H

Pour cold water into the saucepan to a depth of about 2 inches, and put it on the boiling ring or hotplate.

I

Put teaspoonfuls of the mixture on the tray or plate. Use the teaspoon to pat into 'clusters' as in the picture.

J

Add the raisins and *some* of the cornflakes to the chocolate. Stir with the wooden spoon.

K

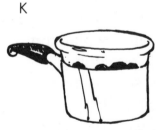

Heat the water until the chocolate melts. Do not stir.

Bubble and Squeak

With the help of Peggy and Amy, Sid is doing his best to look after his pet gerbils, Bubble and Squeak.

The gerbil cage was kept on the living-room table, until the table was needed. Then Sid or Peggy would lift the cage on to the wide window-sill. When the table was clear again, the cage was put back. But sometimes, of course,
5 the children forgot to do that. It did not seem to matter much if the gerbils stayed on the window-sill anyway. There was even room, after dark, to draw the curtains across the windows, between the back of the cage and the window itself.

10 The curtains were rather handsome scarlet ones that Mrs Sparrow had made herself. When they were drawn behind the cage, their folds brushed against the bars at the back.

One morning Mrs Sparrow was down first, as usual, to
15 get breakfast ready. She had raised the blind in the hall, she had brought the milk in from the doorstep, she had gone into the living-room to draw the curtains back . . .

There was a kind of screech from downstairs, and then the repeated screaming of "Sid! Sid! Sid!"
20 It was frightening.

In his school trousers and his pyjama top, Sid flew downstairs. His mother met him at the bottom of the stairs. Tears were streaming down her cheeks; she also looked unspeakably angry. "Come and see what your —
25 your THINGS have done!"

She dragged him into the living-room. The room was still in semi-darkness because the curtains had not yet

been drawn back. But the gloom was shot by strong
beams of light coming through two large ragged holes in
30 the curtains. The holes were just behind the cage, and by
the light through them Sid could see that the inside of the
gerbil cage was littered with scraps and crumbs of scarlet.
One gerbil, sitting up watchfully, seemed to be wiping its
mouth free of a scarlet thread.

The Battle of Bubble and Squeak
Philippa Pearce

1 In which two places was the gerbil cage kept?
2 When was the cage put on the window sill?
3 What was the gerbil doing as Sid entered the room?
4 Who had made the curtains?
5 Write the order of things Mrs Sparrow did when she
   got up.
6 What did Sid see as he came into the room?
7 Why do you think Mrs Sparrow called out for Sid?
8 Do you think Mrs Sparrow liked gerbils? What did
   she call them?
9 What do you think the gerbils have done?
10 In your own words, write down the meaning of these
   words from the passage.

   gloom(line 28)   littered(line 32)   shot by(line 28)
   watchfully(line 33)   handsome(line 10)

Handsome Hare

Here is the start of a story about Hare.

The pieces are not in the right order. Read it and then decide which order the pieces should be in to make sense. Write out your order using the letters at the side of each piece.

Talk with your friends about the order you have decided on.

A   Every morning he spent one hour smartening his fur, another hour smoothing his whiskers, and another cleaning his paws. Then the rest of the day he strutted up and down, admiring his shadow and saying:

B   The other creatures grew so tired of his vain ways that they decided to teach him a lesson. Now they knew that he would believe any story so long as it made him think he was handsome. So this is what they did:

C   "How handsome I am! How amazingly handsome! Surely some great princess will want to marry me soon."

D   Now Hare was a real dandy. He was about the vainest creature on the whole earth.

E   One morning Gazette went up to Hare and said; "Good morning, Hare. How handsome you look. No wonder we've been hearing such stories about you." "Stories?" asked Hare. "What stories?"

How the Whale Became and other stories
Ted Hughes

How do you think the story continues?

Mrs Smith's cupboard

Read this passage, and then draw a picture of the cupboard when Mrs Smith has unloaded her shopping. Make sure you know where everything is going before you start. It might be a good idea to do a rough sketch first.

When she came in from the supermarket struggling with her heavy shopping basket, Mrs Smith carefully put the goods she had bought into the cupboard by the windows over the sink. This cupboard had three shelves
5 and doors which opened wide. At the left hand side of the top shelf she put two packets of cornflakes, separated from two bags of flour by eight packets of tea in two piles. Next came a jar of coffee standing to the left of a large biscuit tin which filled the rest of the shelf out of reach of
10 the children's hands.

  The middle shelf was full of tins apart from two bottles of squash which stood in the middle. To the left of those she stacked six tins of soup in two piles and then at the end of the shelf came two tins of peas and three tins of
15 beans. On the other side of the squash were four smaller tins of baked beans then a larger tin of custard powder. Cans of meat and fish filled the rest of the shelf.

  At the right hand side of the bottom shelf she placed three bags of flour and to the left of them came three jars
20 of jam. Before putting in the box of Oxo cubes, she put in the new can of salt, which just left room for all the jellies except one which she had to put on the top of the baked beans on the middle shelf.

S. Ashworth

Spider and the pot

Spider went out to look for food for his hungry family. He found a magic pot which belonged to old man Thunder.

Spider was overjoyed. He rubbed the pot and said, "Do whatever you would do for the old man Thunder."

At once, the pot was filled with delicious food. There was steaming rice and cassava and meat. Spider ate until
5 he could eat no more. And then he started the long journey back to his village, thinking how happy his family would be.

But as he got closer to home, he began to change his mind. And the closer he got, the more his mind changed.
10 "Why should I share this wonderful pot with anyone?" Spider said to himself. "I shall hide it in a secret place and keep it all for myself."

And that is just what Spider did. He took the magic pot deep into the forest. He dug a hole and put the pot in it
15 and covered the hole with leaves. At night, when everyone was asleep, he took the pot out and ate to his heart's content.

Time passed. Spider's eldest son, Kuma, began to notice that Spider was getting fatter. He was getting fatter
20 and fatter, while everyone else got thinner and thinner. How could this be? Kuma decided to find out.

More Adventures of Spider
Joyce C. Arkhurst

1 What food did the pot make?
2 Where did Spider hide the pot?
3 Who was Kuma?
4 Why do you think Spider's family were hungry?
5 What does the passage tell you about the land where Spider lives?
6 Why does Kuma decide to find out about his father?
7 Why does Spider eat at night?
8 Why do you think Spider changes his mind about sharing the pot?
9 How do you think Kuma will feel when he finds out about the pot?
10 Read the words in this list. Write down the words you think fit Spider.

> good   clever   kind   hungry
> generous   mean   sly   crafty
> helpful   greedy

11 Read the words in this list. Write out the words which you think fit the dry season.

> lush   bare   barren   hard
> soft   dry   green   pleasant

Eruptions

Try to imagine what it is like when a volcano erupts. If you lived nearby, what would you see and feel and hear and smell?

First there might be a trembling of the ground all
5 around the volcano. Rumblings may come from under the ground. We call this an earthquake. To quake means to shiver, so this is really an earth shiver.

This would be a warning that the volcano is getting ready to erupt. There are gases deep down below the
10 ground which are pressing hard to get out.

It is something like blowing up a balloon. The pressure of air inside the balloon gets greater and greater. If you keep blowing, you know what will happen. When the pressure is too great, the balloon bursts.

15 If you stop blowing before it bursts, you can hold it between your finger and thumb and the pressure will stay inside. If you let go then the air will rush out of the neck of the balloon.

The neck of the balloon is like a crater of the volcano.
20 When the pressure below the ground is very great the gas rushes out of the crater. It brings with it melted rock, smoke, fire and red-hot ashes.

Volcanoes
William Hirst

1 What happens first, before a volcano erupts?

2 Why does an earthquake happen?

3 What happens when the pressure inside a balloon gets too great?

4 What happens in a volcano when the pressure gets too great?

5 Why is it not a good idea to live too near a volcano?

6 What would the people do when they heard rumblings from the volcano?

7 What happens to the air in a balloon when you let it go?

8 Write two things you would like to know about volcanoes. Now try to find out the answers.

9 Use a dictionary to find the meaning these words have in the passage. Write down each word and its meaning.

   imagine(line 1)   erupts(line 1)   gases(line 9)
   pressure(line 11)   crater(line 20)   neck(line 17)

10 Look up two of these names in an encyclopaedia or reference book, and write what you find out about them.

   Vesuvius   Fujiyama   Krakatoa
   Pompeii

Paddington hits out

Paddington bear is always getting into trouble with Mr Curry, his next-door neighbour. Here he tries to get a good look at Mr Curry's golfing trousers.

Crouching down to the ground behind Mr Brown's shed, he put his eye to a special knot-hole in the fence which usually gave a very good view of the next-door garden, but to his surprise there was nothing to be seen but a wall of blackness.

Looking most disappointed, Paddington picked up one of Mr Brown's old bean sticks and poked it hopefully through the hole in an attempt to unblock it. As he did so a loud cry of a pain suddenly rang out and he nearly fell over backwards with surprise as the familiar figure of the Browns' neighbour suddenly rose into view on the other side of the fence.

"Bear!" roared Mr Curry as he danced up and down clutching his right eye. "Did you do that on purpose, bear?"

Hastily letting go of the stick, Paddington jumped back in alarm. "Oh, no, Mr Curry," he exclaimed, "I was only trying to unblock the hole. If I'd known you were there I'd have done it much more gently. I mean . . ."

"What's that?" bellowed Mr Curry. "What did you say?"

Paddington gave up trying to explain what he meant as the face on the other side of the fence turned a deep purple.

"I wanted to see your sum trousers, Mr Curry," he said unhappily.

"My what trousers?" repeated Mr Curry.

"Your sum trousers, Mr Curry," said Paddington. "The ones you play golf in."

30 Mr Curry gave Paddington a searching look with his good eye. "If you mean my plus-fours why don't you say so, bear?" he growled.

Paddington Goes to Town
Michael Bond

1 What did Paddington see when he looked through the hole in the fence?

2 Who was in the garden next door?

3 Why was Paddington trying to look into the next-door garden?

4 In your own words tell how Paddington tried to unblock the hole.

5 Why did Mr Curry dance up and down?

6 Why did his face turn a deep purple?

7 What do you think Mr Curry has been practising in his back garden?

8 What was Mr Curry doing when he was poked in the eye?

9 Why do you think Paddington gave up trying to explain what had happened?

10 Read the words in this list. Write down the ones you think fit Paddington.

    funny   sad   happy   curious   fierce
    innocent   harmless   interesting

Your first dog

Read the following passage. Some words have been missed out. Think what those words might be.

Read it again and then write down the words you think should fill the spaces like this:

1 name
2 . . . .
3 . . . .

Hello! My . . .*1*. . . is Spot and I am your first puppy. This is my first time away from my . . .*2*. . . and I am a liggle frightened. Please be very gentle . . .*3*. . . me and give me time to get used to you and my . . .*4*. . . home.

There are a few things you can . . .*5*. . . straight away to make me feel better and happier. First, I need a special . . .*6*. . . to sleep because, like you, I am still young and . . .*7*. . . rest. A dog's basket with a cushion in it would be . . .*8*. . . But an ordinary cardboard box with fairly high sides (not too . . .*9*. . . , because I will want to climb out without hurting myself) is fine too.

Please . . .*10*. . . in a soft pillow or towel for me to sleep on, or even an . . .*11*. . . blanket or sweater. This will keep me warm, which is important . . .*12*. . . I am used to snuggling up to other puppies and my mother.

Remember that my first . . .*13*. . . away from my mother I may feel lonely and need to be . . .*14*. . . . Do not be upset if I whimper or cry on my . . .*15*. . . night or two. I will soon settle down.

Your First Dog
Paul Collan and Steffi Fields

Think about the words you have chosen. Discuss them with your friends.

Helen Keller

Now do the same for this passage about Helen Keller.

Helen Keller lived many years ago. When she was a baby she was very sick. She got better, but she could no longer see or hear — so she never learned to talk. This part of the story is about how she learns to "talk", using her hands.

Helen and Annie wandered in the garden for a while. Then they came . . .1. . . an old pump house. Helen liked to play in its cool dampness. In the . . .2. . . of the floor stood a pump. Annie Sullivan began to . . .3. . . its handle up and down. Soon a steady stream of . . .4. . . came pouring out of its spout. Now she took Helen's hand and held . . .5. . . under the cool flow. W A T E R she spelt into . . .6. . . wet palm

At first Helen pulled away. But then, suddenly, . . .7. . . stopped. A new light seemed to come to her face.

Annie . . .8. . . the look. WATER, she spelt, quickly. WATER! WAT. . . Helen. . .9. . . to spell back. And with each movement her face . . .10. . . brighter. For suddenly she knew!

Helen Keller
Margaret Davidson

The chocolate factory

Willy Wonka is showing the children round his fantastic chocolate factory.

"This is the most important room in the entire factory!" he said. "All my most secret new inventions are cooking and simmering in here! Old Fickelgruber would give his front teeth to be allowed inside just for three minutes! So
5   would Prodnose and Slugworth and all the other rotten chocolate makers! But now, listen to me! I want no messing about when you go in! No touching, no meddling, and no tasting! Is that agreed?"

"Yes, yes!" the children cried. "We won't touch a
10   thing!"

"Up to now," Mr Wonka said, "nobody else, not even an Oompa-Loompa, has ever been allowed in here!" He opened the door and stepped out of the boat into the room. The four children and their parents all scrambled
15   after him.

"Don't touch!" shouted Mr Wonka. "And don't knock anything over!"

Mr Wonka himself suddenly became even more excited than usual, and anyone could see that this was
20   the room he loved best of all. He was hopping about among the saucepans and the machines like a child among his Christmas presents, not knowing which thing to look at first. Then he ran over to another machine, a small shiny affair that kept going phut-phut-phut-phut-
25   phut, and every time it went phut, a large green marble dropped out of it into a basket on the floor. At least it looked like a marble.

"Everlasting Gob-stoppers!" cried Mr Wonka proudly. "They're completely new! I am inventing them for children who are given very little pocket money. You can put an Everlasting Gob-stopper in your mouth and you can suck it and suck it and suck it and it will never get smaller!"

Charley and the Chocolate Factory
Roald Dahl

1 Who are Fickelgruber, Prodnose and Slugworth?
2 Why was Mr Wonka so excited in this room?
3 Who do you think was an Oompa-Loompa?
4 How were the children travelling round the factory?
5 Why is this the most important room in the factory?
6 Write the five things Mr Wonka told the children not to do.
7 How can you tell that this is Mr Wonka's favourite room?
8 Why was Wonka so happy at inventing an everlasting gob-stopper?
9 What happened to these gob-stoppers as you sucked them?
10 At which times was Mr Wonka (a) proud (b) happy (c) stern?
11 Here are three notices Mr Wonka could have put on his door to keep people out. Write out the notices in full.

    Entry proh........ No adm........   No e........

12 What sort of person do you think Willy Wonka was? Why? Would you like to meet him? Why?
13 Do you think an everlasting gob-stopper is a good idea? How might you feel about it after a while?

Indian war bonnets

Red Indian braves were very proud of their war paint and decorations. The head dress was especially important to them.

Indians use feathers from eagles to make their war bonnets. First they had to catch an eagle.

Each tribe had its own way of catching the birds. One tribe dug a pit in the ground at a place where eagles lived.
5　An Indian brave would hide in the pit. Bait, such as a live rabbit or a piece of buffalo meat, was placed on branches across the pit. A hole was left in the branches so that the brave could grab the tail feathers of the bird as it landed and ate the meat. The bird would lose its feathers but was
10　not hurt and it grew new tail feathers later.

Some tribes caught young eagles in the nest. They took the birds back to the Indian village and tied them by a leather thong round the leg. The eagles were kept for their feathers and plucked each time they grew new ones.
15　Indians can collect these feathers, but they are not allowed to wear them until they have won them by a brave deed.

When an Indian did a brave deed he had to tell the old men of the tribe all about it. Other braves must be able to
20　say they saw him do the brave deed. If all the old men agree he has done a brave deed then the Indian may wear an eagle feather in his war bonnet.

To touch the enemy without killing him and escape would be a brave deed, to save the life of another Indian
25　in battle would also count − indeed a brave might be given more than one eagle feather for these deeds.

Indians were very proud of their war bonnets, as our soldiers are of their medals, and they took very great care of them.

1 What did Red Indians use in their war bonnets?
2 How were the young eagles kept captive?
3 Why was the hole left in the branches (paragraph 2)?
4 What did a brave have to do before he could wear eagle feathers?
5 Who decided that a brave could wear the feathers?
6 What were the two ways in which Indians got the eagle feathers they needed?
7 Here are five sentences. Rewrite them in the correct order as the story tells you they happen.

    He told the older braves about it.
    He performed a brave deed.
    The brave collected eagle feathers.
    Other braves said they had seen him do it.
    He was allowed to wear the feathers in his bonnet.

8 Which way of taking feathers do you think was the kindest?
9 Why do you think eagle feathers were chosen as a special sign?
10 Why do you think Red Indians took such care of their war bonnets?
11 How do you think the Indian felt as he hid in the pit?

The magic sweets

Graham Hooper is called Grasshopper because he is small for his age and very lively. His strange Uncle Rudolf gives him some magic sweets for his birthday.

Grasshopper picked out a sweet and popped it in his mouth. He was still sucking away as he came to the small muddy path leading from the lane to his garden gate.

"Mm – tastes a bit minty," he said to himself.

5   Then Grasshopper suddenly realized that he couldn't see over the ferns that lined the path. Something very strange was happpening to him. With every step his body and clothes were shrinking rapidly.

Grasshopper was very frightened. He stopped for a
10 moment to look at his hands.

"They're tiny," he thought. "And it hasn't stopped yet. I'd better run home before it's too late."

He ran as fast as his shrinking legs would carry him. In another minute he was smaller than the nearby stinging
15 nettles. Grasshopper slowed down to pick his way around a puddle that looked like a huge pond. Back on the path again he realized to his relief that he had stopped getting smaller. Now he was only six centimetres tall and his satchel was less than a centimetre square.

20 He paused by a daisy to catch his breath. A large animal burst through the thick grass and came running towards him.

"It's bigger than a lion," he thought in alarm.

Grasshopper tried to hide, but he was so frightened he
25 couldn't move.

Grasshopper and the Unwise Owl
Jim Slater

1 How did the small puddle seem to Grasshopper?
2 Where was he when he was sucking the sweet?
3 What did he notice about his hands?
4 How did he first realise he was getting smaller?
5 Why did he pause in the lane?
6 How did the sweet taste?
7 In your own words tell what happened to Grasshopper when he sucked the sweet.
8 Do you think the animal was really large? Grasshopper was six centimetres tall. What do you think the animal might have been that seemed bigger than a lion?
9 Why do you think Grasshopper decided to run home?
10 Do you think he ran very fast? Why do you think so?
11 Later the story says "To him a song thrush would be as big as a vulture." What might these things seem as big as?

    a fox   a rose bush   a dandelion
    a snail

12 What else do you think magic sweets might do?

Woodland creatures

	Size	Weight	Nursery nest	Litter
Wood mouse	9 centimetres head and body 18 centimetres overall.	About 17 grams	Ball shape made from grass and moss.	About 5 litters each year. Usually 6 babies in a litter.
Red squirrel	39 centimetres	220 – 280 grams	Called a drey. Usually high in a tree. Made from twigs, moss, bark and leaves. Domed or cup-shaped.	1 or 2 litters a year, 3 or 4 babies each litter.
Dormouse	8 centimetres head and body. 14 – 17 centimetres overall.	17 – 42 grams	Bell-like, made of loosely woven grass, leaves, bark and twigs.	Several litters between April and October. Between 3 and 7 babies each litter.

1 Which animal is the heaviest?
2 How could you tell the difference between the nests of a wood mouse and a squirrel?
3 About how many babies would a wood mouse have in a year?
4 Which creature has the bushiest tail?
5 If you wanted to watch one of these animals hunting, which one would you find easiest to watch and why?
6 How does the squirrel spend the winter?
7 What are all three animals good at?
8 The head and body of a wood mouse measure about 9 centimetres. From its nose to the tip of its tail (overall length) measures about 18 centimetres. What does this tell you about its tail?

Food	Appearance	Habits
Seeds, grass, berries, fungi, flowers, nuts, insects, snails.	Large, dark eyes, long, thin tail, brown body, pointed nose, whiskers.	Hunts at night, agile climber. Has good hearing and sense of smell. Grooms itself carefully.
Nuts, cones, berries, fruit fungi, birds' eggs.	Small, furry, long bushy tail, two long back legs, two small front paws. Big front teeth, tufted ears and whiskers.	Hunts by day, marvellous climber in tree tops. Awake during winter, may take naps Hides food in lots of places. Call sounds like "chuck, chuck, chuck".
Nuts, seeds, berries, fruit, bark, insects, eggs or baby birds.	Cross between mouse and squirrel. Large dark eyes, quite bushy tail, brown in colour with white chest.	Hunts at night. Sleeps soundly all winter. All good climber, but needs a lot of rest. Often called a dozy mouse.

9 Which animals eat these for food?

(a) birds' eggs (b) insects
(c) bark (d) fruit

10 Why is the dormouse often called 'dozy mouse'?

11 Find words in the chart which have these meanings

(a) climbs and jumps well (a – – – –)
(b) animals born together (l – – – – –)
(c) makes clean and tidy (g – – – – –)
(d) shaped like a cup (d – – – –)
(e) with hairy bunches (t – – – – –)

The poor man and the doctor

A doctor was sitting at dinner one day when his servant
came in and told him that a poor villager had come with a
cart full of wood. He had unloaded it in the shed at the
end of the yard, and was now waiting to be paid.

5   "Send him in," ordered the doctor, and the poor
carter, removing his hat, stepped into the dining room.

   "How much do I owe you?" asked the doctor.

   "One guinea, if you please, sir," answered the man.

   The doctor gave him the money and then poured out a
10 glass of wine.

   "Here," he said, "you look thirsty. Drink this."

   The man took the wine gladly, and when he had drunk
it, he stood looking at the doctor as he sat at dinner.

   How fine to be a doctor and live like this, he thought. I
15 wonder if I could learn to be a doctor.

   So he told the doctor what was in his mind, and the
doctor said, "I'll tell you what to do. First, sell your horse
and cart, and buy a black gown and wig like mine. Next,
have a plate with your name printed on it to hang up
20 outside your door. What is your name?"

   "My name is Fish," said the poor man.

   "That will never do," said the doctor. "You must call
yourself 'Doctor Knowall'. Have that name painted on a
sign. You'll find people will come along fast enough."

25   So poor Fish thanked the doctor and went off and did
as he had been told. He sold his horse and cart and
bought a doctor's gown and wig. Then he had a sign

hung up outside his house saying: DOCTOR
KNOWALL.

30 Everyone who came that way thought he must be a
very wise man indeed.

The Secret Shoemakers
J. Reeves

1 What was in the cart?
2 How much did the load cost?
3 What was the first thing the carter did when he
   entered the room?
4 Why did the doctor give the carter a glass of wine?
5 What is Fish told to do if he wants to become a
   doctor?
6 Write down two things the doctor does which are
   kind.
7 Why does Fish want to be a doctor?
8 Why do you think the name Fish will not do?
9 Why do you think people thought Dr Knowall was
   wise?
10 What do you think might happen next? Is Fish a
   doctor just because he buys a gown, a wig and
   changes his name?
11 Which parts of the passage tell you that this story
   happened a long time ago?

The magic finger

The girl who is telling this story has a magic finger. When she gets cross with someone, she points her finger at them and changes them into anything she chooses.

Now the one thing that Mr Gregg and his two boys loved to do more than anything else was to go hunting. Every Saturday morning they would take their guns and go off into the woods to look for animals and birds to
5   shoot. Even Philip, who was only eight years old, had a gun of his own.

I can't stand hunting. I just can't stand it. It doesn't seem right to me that men and boys should kill animals just for the fun they get out of it. So I used to try to stop
10   Philip and William from doing it. Everytime I went over to their farm I would do my best to talk them out of it, but they only laughed at me.

I even said something about it once to Mr Gregg, but he just walked on past me as if I weren't there.
15   Then, one Saturday morning, I saw Philip and William coming out of the woods with their father, and they were carrying a lovely young deer.

This made me so cross that I started shouting at them.

The boys laughed and made faces at me, and Mr
20   Gregg told me to go home and mind my own P's and Q's.

Well, that did it!

I saw red.

And before I was able to stop myself, I did something I
25   never meant to do.

I PUT THE MAGIC FINGER ON THEM ALL!

The Magic Finger
Roald Dahl

1 Where do the boys live?
2 When do they go hunting?
3 How old was Philip?
4 What does Mr Gregg most enjoy doing?
5 What did the boys do when the girl shouted at them?
6 Why didn't the girl like hunting?
7 How did she try to get the Greggs to stop shooting animals?
8 What did the Greggs do that made her finally lose her temper?
9 Do you think she meant to point the Magic Finger at the Greggs?
10 The Magic Finger can change people. What do you think happens to the Greggs?
11 Write what you think these phrases mean
   (a) to see red
   (b) I can't stand it.

Persephone

Persephone was the goddess of Spring, her mother Demeter was the goddess of the cornfields. They were very happy together, and the earth was full of flowers and fruit.

5   Then one day Pluto, the god of the Underworld, snatched Persephone and made her live with him in the darkness. Demeter went to the King of the Gods, Zeus, to try and get her daughter back.

Demeter said, "I cannot help the corn to grow tall and 10 ripen to the harvest without Persephone. I miss her so much and I am so unhappy."

Fathers and mothers and children were crying so loudly that Zeus could not bear to hear them. "Persephone has eaten in the Underworld," he said, "sc I 15 cannot take her right away from King Pluto. But she only ate six pomegranate seeds. For six months of the year, therefore, she shall be Queen in the Underworld, but for six months she shall walk through the fields and orchards with her mother, and the grass and the flowers and the 20 trees shall grow green again."

When Persephone came up from the Underworld to meet her mother, the trees put on bright green leaves to welcome her. The flowers opened their buds to call "Persephone", and the grass turned green and waved 25 and whispered, "Persephone". She walked through the fields with her mother and the corn grew under their feet. Spring had come back to the world. And so it is today. When Persephone goes down to the Underworld, trees shed their leaves and all the flowers die. Winter is here. 30 But when she comes back, she brings spring with her; she brings daffodils and daisies and dandelions, and the corn grows green in the fields.

Freda Saxey

1 Who is Demeter?
2 Who kidnapped Persephone?
3 Why does Demeter go to Zeus?
4 What did Persephone eat in the Underworld?
5 What happens to the earth when Persephone comes back to it?
6 What does the passage tell you about Demeter?
7 Why do you think fathers, mothers and children are unhappy when Persephone is in the Underworld?
8 What does Zeus decide will happen to Persephone?
9 What is happening to the plants during the six months Persephone is with the god Pluto?
10 Write down the best six words you can think of which tell us about summer. Do the same for winter.

Grooming

The following paragraphs tell you how to groom a pony. They are not in the right order.

Read them through then decide what order you think they should be in. Write out your order using the letter at the beginning.

A   After every few strokes, run the bristles over the teeth of a curry comb to free them of dirt. Tap the side of the curry comb on the floor to get rid of the grease. Finish with a straw wisp and a cloth to leave a shine on his coat. Use a dandy brush on his mane and tail. The mane comb is used to 'pull' or thin out the hairs.

B   Tie up the pony with a slip-knot in his halter so that if he pulls back, the knot can still be undone. Use a dandy brush first to get the mud off his coat. This brush has stiff bristles and a lot of dust and grease will rise to the surface of his coat when using it. To get rid of this, brush the pony with a soft body brush, using circular strokes to clean the coat and massage the skin.

C   If the pony is being groomed for a special occasion, you may wash his tail and then put on a tail bandage to keep the hairs smooth. Roll a tail bandage with the tapes on the inside and put it on firmly from the top to the bottom of the dock.

D   All ponies must be groomed before they are ridden. If you put a saddle on a dirty pony he can get a sore back from the rubbing of dirt between the leather and his skin.

E   Pick out his feet every day with the hoof pick. Wipe his nostrils and eyes with a damp cloth and clean under his tail with a second damp cloth.

Learning to Ride
Ladybird Books

Discuss your order with your friends.

1 What is the difference between a body brush and a dandy brush?
2 Why should a pony be groomed before it is ridden?
3 How do you put a shine on the pony's coat?
4 What use is the tail bandage?
5 When might the pony 'pull back'?
6 How do you get rid of the grease from the curry comb?
7 Why do you think horse riding is so well liked?

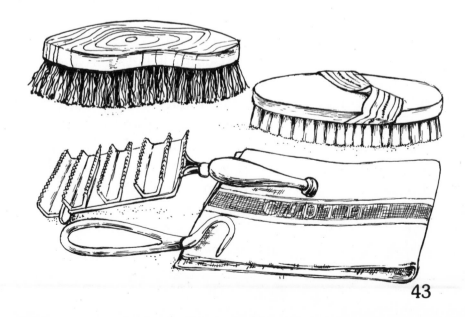

Detective Lucy

Lucy wishes that she was a boy so that she could have adventures. But then she decides that girls can have adventures too, and she becomes a detective.

The workmen were coming out of the house and across the garden back to the door.

Lucy watched them. They had gone into the house carrying nothing, but now their hands were full. The tall
5 young man had a big brown suitcase that weighed him down on one side. Under the other arm he had what looked like a small rolled-up carpet. Ratface had another carpet over one shoulder and he had two smaller suitcases in his hands.

10 They went through the door in the wall; they looked up and down the lane; then they opened the back of the van and put the suitcases and the carpets inside. As they went back to the house, they were laughing. Lucy heard them talking. "Dead easy." "All those bags is a gift."
15 "Help yourself!" they said. Lucy lay very still on the wall and thought.

Next time they came out they had a trunk. It was so big and so heavy they had to carry it between them, and once they set it down on the lawn the Ratface mopped
20 his face and swore. He said, "I'm not fetching any more."

The tall young man said, "What about the pictures?"

Ratface said, "Too risky." But the tall young man said something like, "Clobber will see to that," and then he and Ratface picked up the trunk again and they argued
25 about pictures all the time they were hoisting it into the van.

Lucy
Catherine Storr

1 What did the two men argue about?
2 What did the men carry going into the house?
3 What did the men do *after* they went through the door in the wall and *before* they came out again with the trunk?
4 Why were the men laughing as they went back?
5 Why do you think Lucy thought they were workmen at first?
6 How could Lucy tell that the young man's suitcase was heavy?
7 Why do you think they looked up and down the lane?
8 What is happening in the story? Who are the men? What should Lucy do? What do you think will happen next?
9 Find words in the passage that mean the same as

    lifted   observed   wiped   simple

10 The suitcase is big and brown. How could you describe these suitcases?

The witch who lived on the motorway

This story is about a wicked witch who lived on a motorway.

They don't usually let people live on motorways, but this witch's cottage had been there centuries before the motorway was laid and she had refused to move from it. Several important people had tried to make her change her mind, but she had done so many nasty things to them with her magic that they decided in the end to leave her alone.

So there she stayed, full of spiteful tricks and harmful ideas for dealing with anyone who bothered her. Her tumbledown cottage with its grimy brickwork was a disgrace to the tidy carriageways and graceful new bridges, and her weed-choked garden a blot on the neat verges.

By day the sight of her dirty face glaring from a window filled the passing drivers with dread, and at night time, when she brewed her spells, the steam from her iron pot ran like mist along the road surface as far as the nearest service station where it spoiled the taste of the tea and sandwiches in the Transport Cafeteria and made the lorry drivers grumble.

At first the authorities erected signs along the track saying things like *Beware! Witch 20m Ahead. No stopping* — with a black cut-out of a hook-nosed witch on a broomstick underneath for the benefit of foreigners, and drivers who couldn't read. The one before you reached her was enormous:

WITCH ¼ MILE AHEAD
STOP AT YOUR PERIL!

The Magician Who Kept a Pub
Dorothy Edwards

1 Who tried to persuade the witch to move?
2 Why did they leave her alone after that?
3 Who ate in the Transport Cafeteria?
4 How did the witch spend her time by day and by night?
5 How could foreigners tell there was a witch about?
6 How far away from the witch's house was the first sign?
7 Write down all that the passage tells you about the witch's house and garden.
8 How do you think the witch felt when a motorway was built near her house?
9 What was the last sign telling drivers not to do? Why should they not do this?
10 What would you have written on the signs to warn people?
11 Look at the words in this list.

neat   new   old   dirty
graceful   neglected   overgrown
tumbledown

Make two lists. Put all the words which describe the motorway in one list and those for the witch's cottage in the other.

First published in 1982 by Basil Blackwell Limited
Reprinted seven times

Reprinted in 1992, 1993, 1994 by
Simon & Schuster Education

Reprinted in 1995 by
Stanley Thornes (Publishers) Ltd
Ellenborough House
Wellington Street
CHELTENHAM GL50 1YD
England

A catalogue record for this book is available from the British Library

ISBN 0 7487 2264 5

Printed in Hong Kong by Wing King Tong Co. Ltd.